BRYAN **ADAMS** THE BE E

BRYAN **ADAMS** THE BE E

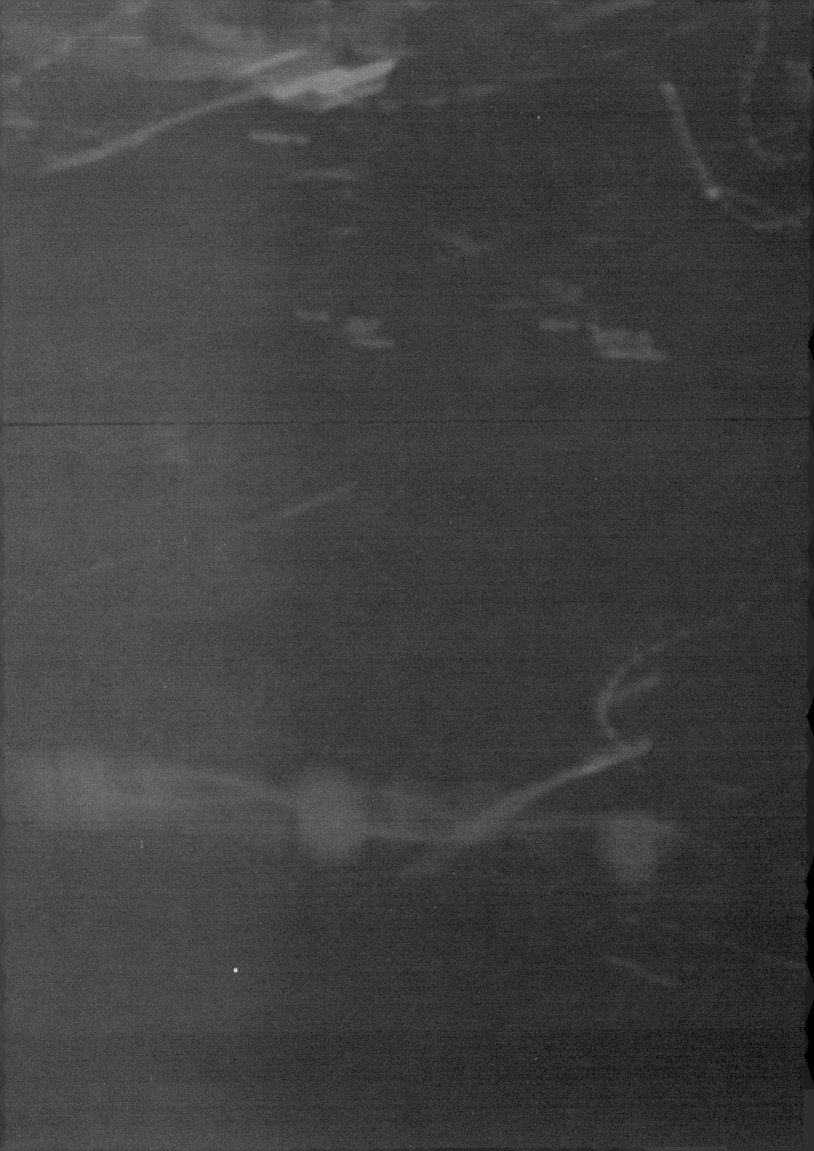

BRYAN **ADAMS** THE BEST OF ME

BRYAN **ADAMS** THE BEST OF ME

WISE PUBLICATIONS
london / new york / sydney / paris / copenhagen / madrid / tokyo

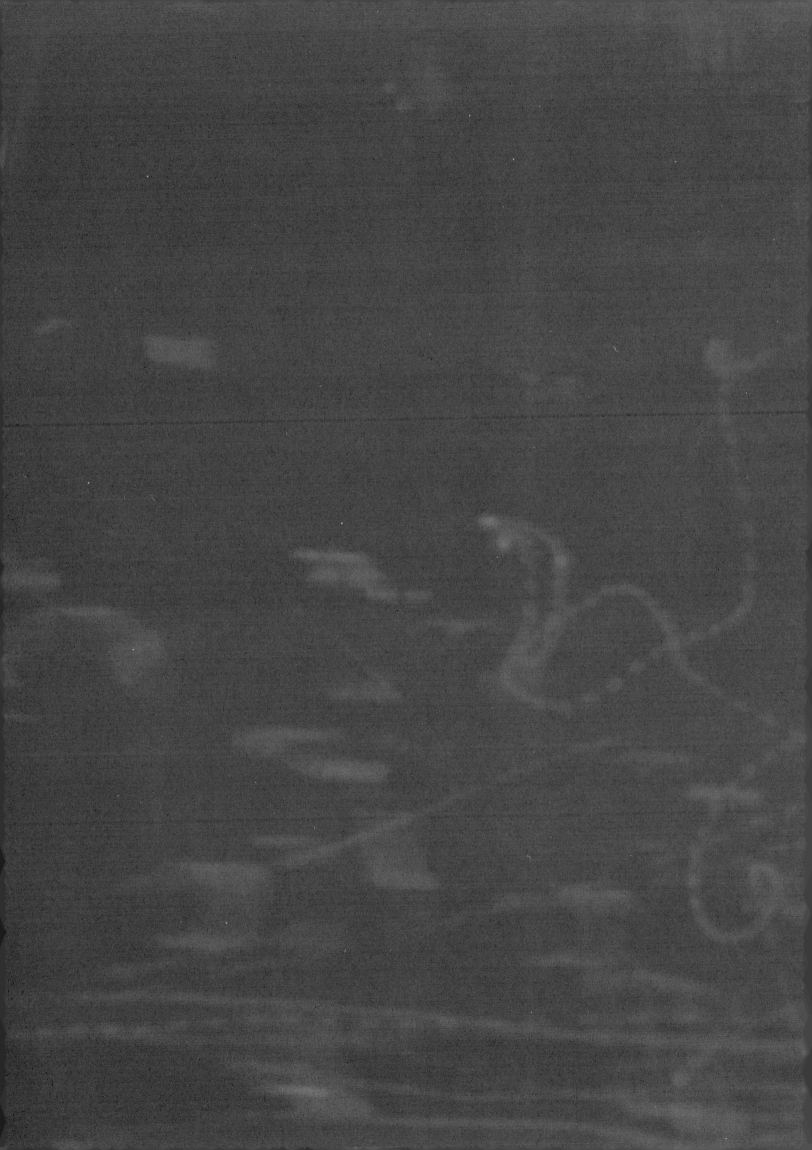

exclusive distributors:
music sales limited, 8/9 frith street, london w1v 5tz, england.
music sales pty limited, 120 rothschild avenue, rosebery, nsw 2018, australia.

order no. am962753
isbn 0-7119-8038-1
this book © copyright 1999 by wise publications.

music arranged by derek jones.
music engraved by paul ewers music design.

printed in the united kingdom by caligraving limited, thetford, norfolk.

your guarantee of quality:
as publishers, we strive to produce every book to the highest commercial standards.
the music has been freshly engraved and the book has been carefully
designed to minimise awkward page turns and to make playing from it a real pleasure.
particular care has been given to specifying acid-free, neutral-sized paper made from pulps
which have not been elemental chlorine bleached.
this pulp is from farmed sustainable forests and was produced with special regard for the environment.
throughout, the printing and binding have been planned to ensure a sturdy,
attractive publication which should give years of enjoyment.
if your copy fails to meet our high standards, please inform us and we will gladly replace it.

music sales' complete catalogue describes thousands of titles and is
available in full colour sections by subject, direct from music sales limited.
please state your areas of interest and send a cheque/postal order for £1.50 for postage to:
music sales limited, newmarket road, bury st. edmunds, suffolk ip33 3yb.

www.musicsales.com

THE BEST OF ME 9

CAN'T STOP THIS THING WE STARTED 14

I'M READY 22

SUMMER OF '69 27

LET'S MAKE A NIGHT TO REMEMBER 32

ALL FOR LOVE 42

HAVE YOU EVER REALLY LOVED A WOMAN 47

RUN TO YOU 52

CLOUD NUMBER NINE 57

(EVERYTHING I DO) I DO IT FOR YOU 70

BACK TO YOU 64

WHEN YOU'RE GONE 75

PLEASE FORGIVE ME 80

THE ONLY THING THAT LOOKS GOOD ON ME IS YOU 87

INSIDE OUT 92

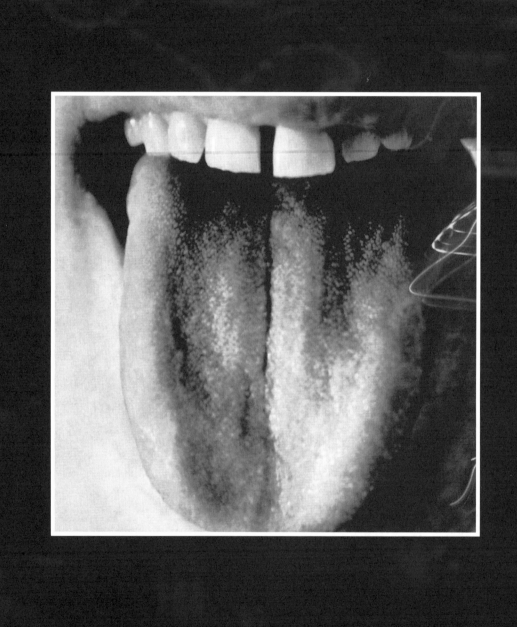

THE BEST OF ME

words & music by bryan adams & robert john 'mutt' lange

Verse 2:
I may not always know what's right
But I know I want you here tonight.
Gonna make this moment last for all your life.
Yeah, oh this is love; an' it really means so much
I can tell from every touch.
No, no, no, can't get enough.

When you want it, when you need it
You'll always have the best of me.
I can't help it; believe it
You'll always get the best of me.

CAN'T STOP THIS THING WE STARTED

words & music by bryan adams & robert john 'mutt' lange

You might stop a hur - ri - cane,— might ev - en stop the
(Verse 2 see block lyric)

driv - in' rain.— You might have a doz - en oth - er— guys,— but if

you wan - na stop— me ba - by, don't ev - en try.— I'm go - in' one_____ way:—

your____ way.____ Well it's such_ a

strong_____ way,_____ let's make it our_____ way._____

Now, ba - by,_____ can't stop this

thing we start - ed,_____ God knows_____ we're right._____

I can't stop this course we plot - ted,_____ yeah;_____

this thing called love, we got it. ___ Ain't no place for the

brok - en heart - ed. I can't stop it, can't stop.

Can't stop this thing we start - ed, ___ you got - ta know

___ it's ___ al - right. Can't stop this course we plot - ted, ___

oh—— yeah.

Can't stop it,

Repeat to fade

can't stop it, can't— stop it, yeah, yeah.

Verse 2:

You might stop the world spinnin' around
Might even walk on holy ground.
I ain't Superman and I can't fly
But if you wanna stop me, baby
Don't even try.
I'm goin' one way: your way.
It's such a strong way, let's make it our way.

Now baby, can't stop this thing we started
You gotta know it's right.
I can't stop this course we plotted;
This thing called love, we got it.
No place for the broken-hearted.
I can't stop this thing we started
No way, I'm goin' your way.

I'M READY

words & music by bryan adams & jim vallance

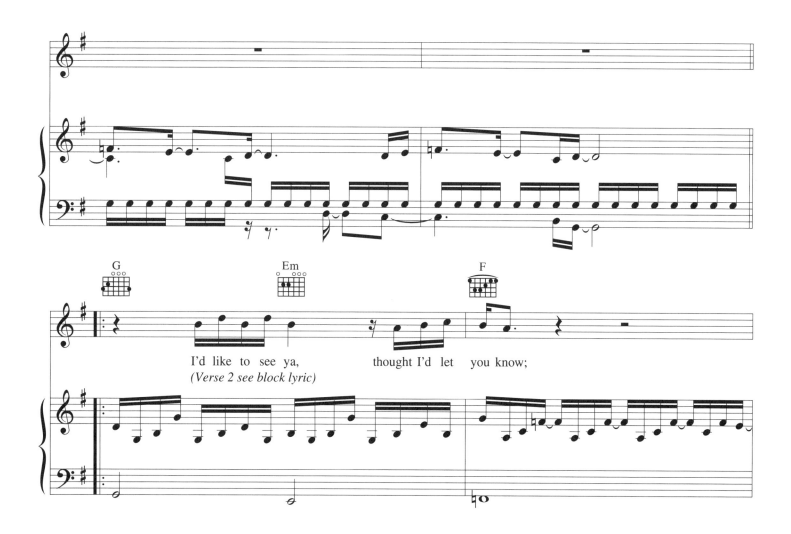

I'd like to see ya,   thought I'd let   you know;
(Verse 2 see block lyric)

I wan-na be with you ev-'ry day.

'Cause I got a feel-in' that's be-gin-nin' to grow,

an' there's on-ly one thing I can say: I'm read-

-y to love you, I'm read-

Verse 2:
You left me a long note when you left me here.
You told me that love was hard to find.
But baby, it's easy and I'll make it clear
There's only one thing on my mind.
I'm ready, *etc.*

SUMMER OF '69

words & music by bryan adams & jim vallance

1. Me— and some guys from school had a band and we tried real hard.
(Verses 2 & 3 see block lyric)

Jim-my quit and Jo-dy got mar-ried.— I should-a known we'd

nev-er get far. Oh, when I look back now,—

that sum-mer seemed to last for-ev-er, and— if I

had the choice,— yeah,— I'd al - ways wan - na be there.

Those— were the best days of my— life.

To Coda ⊕ | **1.**

2.

Back in the sum - mer of six - ty nine.—

Man,— we were kill-in' time, we were young and rest-less, we need-ed to— un wind.

I guess noth-in' can last— for-ev-er, for-ev-er,— no!

⊕ *Coda*

Back in the sum - mer of six - ty nine. __

Repeat ad lib. to fade

Back in the sum - mer of

Verse 2:

Ain't no use in complainin' when you got a job to do
Spent my evenin's down at the drive-in, and that's when I met you
Standin' on your mama's porch, you told me that you'd wait forever
Oh, and when you held my hand, I knew that it was now or never
Those were the best days of my life.

Verse 3:

And now the times are changin', look at everything that's come and gone
Sometimes when I play that old six-string I think about you, wonder what went wrong
Standin' on your mama's porch, you told me it'd last forever
Oh, and when you held my hand, I knew that it was now or never
Those were the best days of my life.

LET'S MAKE A NIGHT TO REMEMBER

words & music by bryan adams & robert john 'mutt' lange

1. I love the way you look to-night,—
(Verse 2 see block lyric)

with your hair hang-in' down on your shoul-ders.—

ren - der.   Let's make a night   to re -

mem - ber   all   life   long._____

long._____

Oh___ well I think a - bout you all of the time,___ can't you___ see, you drive me out o' my mind.___ Well, I'm___

never holdin' back a - gain, yeah, I

never want this night to end. 'Cos I've

never touched some - bo - dy like the way I touch your bo - dy, now I

never wan - na let your bo - dy go. Let's make a

(ad lib. vocal)

Play 5 times for fade

Verse 2:

I love the way you move tonight,
Beads of sweat drippin' down your skin,
Me lyin' here an' you lyin' there,
Our shadows on the wall and our hands everywhere.

Let's make out, let's do something amazing.
Let's do something that's all the way.
'Cos I've never touched somebody
Like the way I touch your body,
Now I never wanna let your body go.

Let's make a night to remember, *etc.*

ALL FOR LOVE

words & music by bryan adams, robert john 'mutt' lange & michael kamen

HAVE YOU EVER REALLY LOVED A WOMAN?

words & music by bryan adams, robert john 'mutt' lange & michael kamen

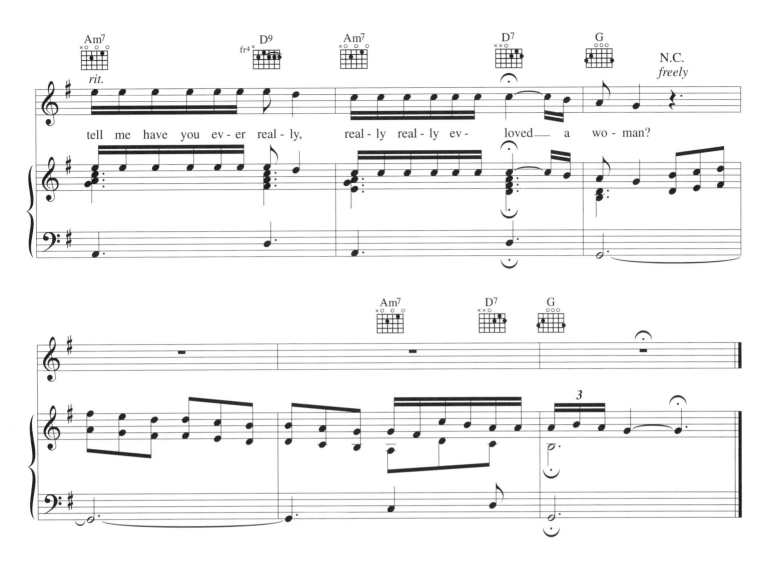

tell me have you ev-er real-ly, real-ly real-ly ev- loved___ a wo-man?

Verse 2:
To really love a woman, let her hold you
Till you know how she needs to be touched.
You've gotta breathe her, really taste her,
Till you can feel her in your blood.
And when you can see your unborn children in her eyes,
You know you really love a woman.

When you love a woman
You tell her that she's really wanted.
When you love a woman
You tell her that she's the one.
She needs somebody to tell her
That you'll always be together
So tell me have you ever really,
Really really loved a woman.

Verse 3:
Instrumental

Then when you find yourself
Lyin' helpless in her arms,
You know you really love a woman.

When you love a woman *etc.*

RUN TO YOU

words & music by bryan adams & jim vallance

But that-'d change if she ev-er found out a-bout you and I.

Oh, but her love is cold._____

It would-n't hurt her if she did-n't know.__ 'Cause when it

gets too much__ I need to feel your touch. I'm gon-na

Verse 2:

She's got a heart of gold
She'd never let me down
But you're the one that always turns me on
And keep me comin' round.
I know her love is true
But it's so damn easy makin' love to you.
I got my mind made up
I need to feel your touch.

I'm gonna run to you *etc.*

CLOUD NUMBER NINE

words & music by bryan adams, max martin & gretchen peters

(Num-ber nine.____) (Num-ber nine.____) (Num-ber nine.____) (Num-ber nine.

(Num-ber nine.____) (Num-ber nine.____) (Num-ber nine.____)

1. Clue num-ber one____ was when you knocked on my door,____ clue num-ber two____ was____ the

(Verse 2 see block lyric)

look that you wore;____ an' that's when I knew,____ it was a pret-ty good sign,____ that

D.%. al Coda

✛ *Coda*

N.C.

Yeah, we can watch the world___ go by___

___ up on cloud___ num - ber nine.___

Verse 2:
Now he hurt you and you hurt me
And that wasn't the way it was supposed to be
So, baby, tonight let's leave the world behind
And spend some time up on cloud number nine.

Well, it's a long way up *etc.*

BACK TO YOU

words & music by bryan adams & eliot kennedy

that I could not see,— I've want-ed things— that were out of— reach.—

An' then I— found you— an' you helped— me through;— yeah, you showed—

— me what to— do.— An' that's— why—

I'm com-in' back to— you,— yeah.— Like a star—

that guides a ___ ship ___ a - cross the o - cean, ___

that's how your love ___ will take me ___ home ___ back to ___ you. ___

An', if I wish ___ up - on ___ that star, ___

___ some - day I'll ___ be where ___ you are. ___ Yeah, I know

that day is com-in' soon; yeah, I'm com-

-in' back to you.

1.

2.

2. You've been a-lone,

Might've let

Verse 2:
You've been alone but you did not show it.
You've been in pain when I did not know it.
You let me do what I needed to
You were there when I needed you.
Might've let you down, might've messed you around
But you never changed your point of view.
An' that's why I'm comin' back to you.

Like a star *etc.*

(EVERYTHING I DO) I DO IT FOR YOU

words by bryan adams & robert john 'mutt' lange
music by michael kamen

Look in-to my eyes, you will see
(Verse 2 see block lyric)

what you mean to me. Search your heart, search your

soul, _____ and when you find_ me there you'll search_ no_ more. Don't

tell me it's not worth try-ing for, you can't tell me it's not worth dy-in'

for. You know it's true,_ ev-'ry-thing I_ do,_ I do it for_

1.
_ you.

2.
_ you. There's

no love   like   your love,   and no   oth - er   could give

more   love.   There's   no - where   un - less   you're there   all   the

time,_____   all   the   way,   yeah._____

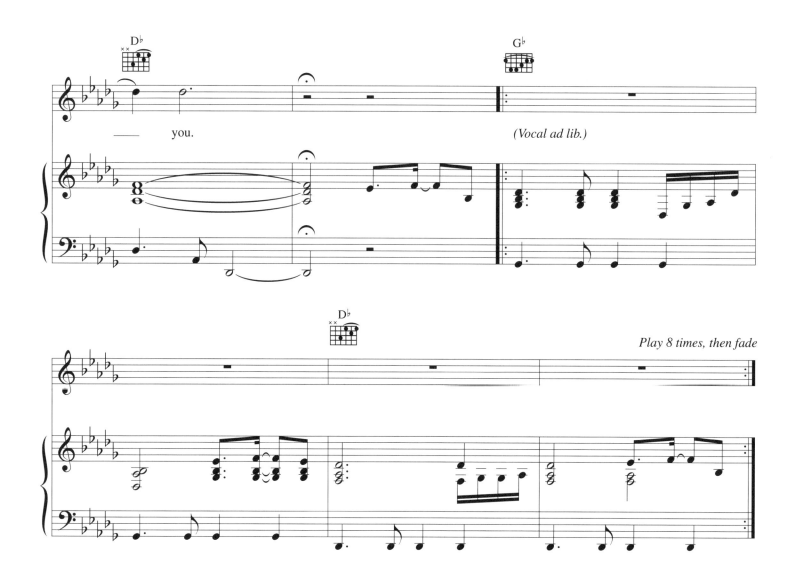

Verse 2:
Look into your heart, you will find
There's nothin' there to hide.
Take me as I am, take my life
I would give it all, I would sacrifice.
Don't tell me it's not worth fightin' for
I can't help it, there's nothin' I want more.
You know it's true, everything I do
I do it for you.

WHEN YOU'RE GONE

words & music by bryan adams & eliot kennedy

To Coda ⊕

wrong,   ba - by,   when you're   gone.___

2. I've been driv-

(Or ad lib. solo)

78

Verse 2:
I've been drivin' up an' down these streets
Tryin' to find somewhere to go
Yeah, I'm lookin' for a familiar face, but there's no one I know
Oh, this is torture, this is pain; it feels like I'm gonna go insane
I hope you're comin' back real soon, 'cause I don't know what to do.

Baby, when you're gone, *etc.*

PLEASE FORGIVE ME

words & music by bryan adams & robert john 'mutt' lange

The one thing I'm sure— of is the way we made—— love. The one thing I de-pend— on if we're asked to stay———— on. With ev-'ry word and ev-'ry breath— I'm pray- -ing.—— That's why I'm say - ing,———————— Please for -

Verse 2:
It still feels like our best times are together
Feels like the first touch
We're still getting closer baby
Can't get close enough.
Still holding on, you're still number one.
I remember the smell of your skin
I remember everything
I remember all your moves
I remember you, yeah.
I remember the nights, you know I still do.

So if you're feeling lonely don't *etc.*

THE ONLY THING THAT LOOKS GOOD ON ME IS YOU

words & music by bryan adams & robert john "mutt" lange

don't look good_ in no Ar-ma-ni suits,_ no Guc-ci shoes_ or de-
(Verse 2 see block lyric)

sign-er boots._ I've tried the lat-est lines from A to Z,__ but there's

just one thing_ that looks good on me.__ The on-ly thing I want,_

__ the on-ly thing I need,__

the on-ly thing I choose,— yeah, the on-ly thing— that looks

good on me —— is you.——

2. I'm not

Yeah— it's you,—— it could on-ly be——

Verse 2:
I'm not satisfied with Versace's style,
Put those patent leather pants in the circular file.
Sometimes I think I might be looking good,
But there's only one thing that fits like it should.

INSIDE OUT

words & music by bryan adams & gretchen peters

Verse 2:
The saddest song you ever heard
The most you said with just one word
The loneliest prayer you ever prayed
The truest vow you ever made
What makes you laugh, what makes you cry
What makes you mad, what gets you by
Your highest high, your lowest low
These are the things I wanna know.

I wanna know you *etc.*